# The Gorilla
## Did It !

**More Poems
For The Kid
In All Of Us**

# Arnot McCallum
## Illustrated by Glen Girard

First publishing  January 2000
Second publishing  June 2001
Third publishing  April 2003
Fourth publishing  December 2005

primrose publishing

primrose publishing
654 Primrose Place Tecumseh
Ontario Canada N8N 4C8
(519) 735-0330 e-mail arnot@MNSi.net


Canadian Cataloguing in Publication Data

McCallum, Arnot, 1932-
    The gorilla did it! : more poems for the kid in all

of us

ISBN 0-9683178-1-2


    1. Children's poetry, Canadian (English)
I. Girard, Glen  II. Title.

PS8575.C373G67 1999    jC811'.54   C99-901674-1
PZ7.M12296Go 1999

# Contents

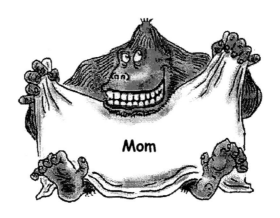

Mom

For my Mother,
For your Mother
And all the wonderful
Moms of the world.

# The Gorilla Did It!

There's a hairy old Gorilla
Underneath my bed.
He stole the baby's teddy bear,
And painted it bright red.

Gorilla hid that bubble gum
In my father's running shoe.
Gorilla stuck the toilet seat
With sticky, Super Glue.

Gorilla 'smushed' that jelly juice
Into my Brother's hair.
Gorilla put the thumb tack
On Mr. Wilson's chair.

Gorilla put those wiggly worms
In grandpa's pork and beans.
Gorilla cut the pockets off
My Sister's brand new jeans.

Gorilla hid that bullfrog
In my Grandma's dresser drawer.
Gorilla tracked his muddy feet
Across the kitchen floor.

My Mom says...
"Stop blaming that Gorilla
For those awful things you do.
Or, you and that Gorilla,
**Will be living in the zoo!** "

# Ants

Did you ever find ants
In your kitchen?
Did you ever find ants
On your head?
Did you ever find ants
In your lunchbox?
Did you ever find ants
In your bed?

Did you ever find ants
In the sugar?
Did you ever find ants
On your doll?
But the worst kind of ants
Are the ants in your pants.
That's the worst kind of all.

# Secret Valentine

I have a secret valentine.
She sits in front of me.
I don't know where she lives,
But her name is Rose Marie.

She's blonde and tall and beautiful.
She's smart, and really cool.
She's just about the prettiest girl,
In this entire school.

I've got to keep my secret.
I can't tell anyone.
'Cause...
Rose Marie's my teacher,
And I'm in her Grade One.

# Arn, Get On That Potty!

My Mom bought me a potty.
She said that I was ready
To sit on it,
And learn to 'go'
Just like my cousin Freddy.

But...
I really like my diaper.
It's soft upon my skin.
It helps to keep the cold wind out,
And keep the 'bad stuff' in.

So...
I won't use that potty.
It's just not right for me.
But that potty's really very nice
**To sit on, and watch T.V.**

# Baby Nan

I had a little brother.
I called him Baby Nan.
I stuck him on the ceiling,
And tied him to the fan.

The fan went 'round,
And 'round and 'round.
At such a dizzy pace.
Now Baby Nan is orbiting
**'Way up in outer space.**

# Sister Sarah

My baby sister Sarah,
Found Dad's tube of Super Glue.
Now Mother's stuck on the toilet seat,
We don't know what to do.

She's been sitting there since Saturday,
She's angry, and she's beat,
But, the Firemen will soon be here,
To lift her off the seat!

# A Promise Is Forever

A promise is a promise.
A promise is forever.
A promise means you won't forget.
**Never... Never... Never.**

When I was five and just a boy,
A playmate broke my favourite toy.
You promised me you'd fix it fast,
You did, before the day had passed.

At nine the bully of the town,
Ripped my shirt and pushed me down.
You promised me that very day.
You made the bully stay away.

High school was a time for girls
With pretty looks and pretty curls.
You promised me we'd stay up late.
Hit the books, and graduate.

I married. Soon we had a boy.
My son became my pride and joy.
You promised me you'd love him too.
You loved my son, and he loved you.

Now your eyes are growing dim.
You've lost your vigor.
Lost your vim.
Don't worry Dad,
I'll still be there
To give you love and tender care.
I promise.

A promise is a promise.
A promise is forever.
A promise means you won't forget.
**Never... Never... Never.**

# I love you Dad.

7

# Tattle Tale

My sister is a Tattle Tale.
She always watches me.
There's nothing I can keep from her,
There's nothing she can't see.

She told my Mom I broke that cup
And hid it on the shelf.
She didn't have to squeal on me.
I was going to tell, myself.

I found my sister's diary
And took a little peek.
My sister told my Father.
I was grounded for a week.

My sister told the principal
That I kissed Sally Brown.
He called her Dad... her Dad got mad.
He chased me through the town

Don't get me wrong, I love my Sis.
But someday very soon,
I'm going to stuff her in a box,
**And send her**
        **to the moon.**

# Baloney Maloney

His name was Baloney Maloney.
He had big trouble telling the truth.
He said he could make us all disappear.
Simply by rubbing his tooth.

He said he was really a millionaire,
Who had a fine house and a car.
He said he once wrestled a Grizzly Bear.
His Dad was a Rock and Roll Star.

He said he was once on a rocket ship,
He took a wild ride to the Moon.
He said that he owned a big submarine.
We'd all get a ride... very soon.

We all knew Baloney was fibbing.
But... really, we kids didn't care.
'Cause Baloney told wonderful stories,
That were awesome, and special and rare.

Now...
We never see Baloney Maloney.
We all moved away to new homes.
Baloney Maloney's a writer.
He tells stories,
And writes children's poems.

# Bells

Some kids like to hear the bells
On the top of our church steeple.
Some kids like to hear the bells
That ring out to the people.
Some kids like those wedding bells
That sing of love and joy.
Some kids like the school bells
Calling every girl and boy.
Some kids like the jingle bells
That hang on Santa's sleigh.
Some kids like the special bells
We hear on Christmas Day.
But...
The bells that make me  happy.
The bells that bring me luck,
Are those tiny little tinkle bells.

**Here comes the Ice Cream Truck !**

# Big Sister

My older sister sleeps with me.
She rolls around in bed.
She hogs the covers.
Passes gas.
And slobbers on my head.

Her toes are full of toe jam.
Her face is full of cream.
Her breath smells bad.
She snores all night.
She makes me want to scream.

Some night she's going to roll on me,
And squash me like a bug,
They'll never find my body,
Just a grease spot on the rug.

11

# Captured By Giants

I've been captured by some giants,
They're smiling down at me.
They're awful strong and awful tall,
As giants 'oughta' be.

The big guy seems to like me.
He tickles on my toes.
He tickles on my belly
And, he tickles on my nose.

But... he's driving me half crazy.
If only I could shout
I'd tell that ugly giant guy
"Hey buddy, cut it out."

They're always fussing over me
With silly baby talk.
They feed me milk and gooey stuff
And try to make me walk.

The giants keep close tabs on me
They make me wear a bib.
At night the giants lock me up
In a cage they call a crib.

I'm going to make a break for it.
I've got a super plan.
I'll grab the giant's car keys
And take off in his van.

# Captain Rub-A-Dub

When I grow up
I'm going to be,
A pirate
On the briny sea.

I'll have a beard.
A pirate hat.
A pirate ship.
A pirate cat.

A pirate sword.
A pirate hook.
A pirate crew.
A pirate cook.

Buckle shoes.
Socks knee high.
A pirate patch
On one bad eye.

A parrot sitting
On my hand.
A treasure chest
In every land.

My Mom says,
"Captain Rub-A-Dub.
Just be a pirate
In your own bathtub."

# Christmas Dinner

Our presents were all Christmas hits.
Dad's happy with his leather mitts.
The bike was 'cool'.
The tie a winner.
But...
Where will we eat Christmas dinner?
We have two Grandmas.
Both want us there.
But...
We just can't be everywhere.
They have two turkeys.
They have four wings.
Four legs with tons of giblet things.
Tons of gravy in each pot,
Tons of potatoes,
Mashed and hot.
Each Gram will bake a pie and cake.
Guaranteed to make your tummy ache.
Each Gram will smile and sweetly say,
"See you all on Christmas Day."
I love my Grams.
That's really true.
So...
I think I know just what to do.
A wise solution came to me.
I'm going to 'clone' our family.

# Christmas Puppy

I'm a Christmas Puppy
I'm underneath the tree.
I'm all wrapped up
In polka dots.
I sure hope they like me.

I've been waiting very patiently
For someone to wake up,
And come downstairs
To find me here.
I'm a frightened Christmas Pup.

I'm really very lonely.
I really miss my mother.
I really miss my sister.
And I really miss my brother.

Hey wait, my world looks brighter.
Here comes a little boy.
He's hugging me,
And petting me.
My heart is full of joy.

It's great to have somebody
To share a meaty bone.
And now I have a little boy
And a family of my own.

# Circus, Circus

The Circus is coming to town today
The Circus is coming to town.
With lions and tigers
And elephants,
With horses and ponies and clowns.

I'll look for the Man
On the Flying Trapeze
Swinging up higher and higher.
I'll watch for the girl
With the green parasol
Dancing across the High Wire.

I'll take a neat ride
On an elephant's back.
Eat candy apples and floss.
I'll put on the Ringmaster's
Jacket and hat
And pretend that I am the Boss.

And when I'm asleep
I'll dream pleasant dreams,
Of sights that are
Awesome and rare.
I'll be under the light
At the Big Top tonight
With my dolly
And my teddy bear.

The Circus is coming to town today.
The Circus is coming to town.
With lions and tigers
And elephants,
With horses and ponies and clowns.

# Ponies Prance

Girls skip.
Icicles drip.
Roads ramble.
Bears amble.
Soldiers stride.
Penguins glide
Kangaroos jump.
Ghosts bump.
Lizards leap.
Bugs creep.
Eyes wink.
Snakes slink.
Ponies prance.
But...
I dance.

# Cowboy Teddy

I'm a Cowboy Teddy Bear.
I ride a rocking horse.
He's very gentle, never bites.
He's really fast of course.

I'm a Cowboy Teddy Bear.
I wear leather cowboy boots.
I have a water pistol
That really squirts and shoots.

I'm a Cowboy Teddy Bear.
I wear a cowboy hat.
I rope the cows and brand them.
Now what do you think of that?

I'm a Cowboy Teddy Bear.
I have a cowboy bed.
I have cowboy pyjamas,
And a scarf of Cowboy red.

I'm a Cowboy Teddy Bear.
I'm wild and strong and free.
I hope someday your Mom buys you
A Cowboy just like me.

# Fingers

I have TEN little fingers.
They're sitting on my hand.
They're great for counting money,
And building castles in the sand.

I use them when I tickle.
I use them when I scratch.
I use them when I'm pointing,
And I use them when I catch.

They're great for counting pennies,
And picking ear wax from my ears.
They're great for making mud pies.
And wiping salty tears.

But...
Sometimes I use my fingers
And make my Mommy scream.
It's when I stick my fingers
In her bowl of whipping cream.

# Dogs

Large dogs,
Fat dogs,
Happy, floppy, mat dogs.
Rough, tough, guard dogs,
These are just a few.
Silly dogs,
Frilly dogs,
Pretty, willy-nilly dogs,
Furry, skinny, house dogs,
Loyal, friendly too.
Sled dogs,
Red dogs,
Don't forget unfed dogs.
But best of all when day is done,
I like sleep-in-bed dogs.

# Did You Hear The Latest?

Did you hear the latest?
They're using soda pop
To fill the water fountains
That run and never stop.

They're making chocolate broccoli
And butterscotch green beans.
The pit bulls will have rubber teeth
And teachers will wear jeans.

Every kid will have a room
That they can call their own.
And every kid in every house
Will have a telephone!

But last of all, the very best,
They're closing all the schools.
Hey, don't believe a word I say
'Cause...

## This is April Fools!

Heh
Heh
Heh

# Flowers

My house is filled with flowers.
Yellow, blue and red.
I found them on the hillside,
And by the river bed.

I found some in the valley.
Some flourished in the dells.
I picked some yellow Daisies,
And some purple Heather Bells.

Together in a bright bouquet
My flowers seemed to glow.
Like a beautiful soft sunset,
Or a heavenly rainbow.

Our children are like flowers.
Many colours, many faces.
Growing strong around the world,
In many different places.

The world is like a garden.
Each child a flower there.
**And every child is precious,**
**Unique, and fine, and rare.**

# Germs

Germs are not my favourite topic
Because you see,
They're microscopic.
Germs are wiggly, squiggly things.
They don't have legs.
They don't have wings.
They're not too big.
They're very small.
You really can't see them at all.

They make us barf.
They make us sneeze.
They make us cough.
They make us wheeze.
So...
Wash your hands.
Wash your toes.
Wash your ears.
Wash your nose.
These ugly germs are everywhere.
In the water, in the air.
But...
The biggest germ sleeps down the hall.
**I'm talking about my brother, Paul.**

# Grade Nine's Really Cool

I forgot to do my homework.
I didn't catch the bus.
An ugly 'zit' sits on my nose.
It's filled with toxic pus.
My blouse is full of mustard stains.
My hair's a tangled mess.
I'm like the Bride of Frankenstein,
But uglier, I guess.
My lockers jammed.
I'm late for class.
My book report is due.
I got an 'F' in History.
I'm failing English too.
I'm not so good at basketball.
I didn't make the team.
I broke my arm in Gym Class,
Falling off the balance beam.
But...
I think High School's awesome.
I love to go to school.
'Cause I'm a big Grade Niner now,
And...

**Grade Nine's really cool.**

# Grandpa

My Grandpa takes me to the lake.
We boat, and fish, and swim.
My Grandpa is a Super Guy.
I love to be with him.

Sometimes he calls me up and says,
"Two tickets for the game."
Sometimes he can't come over,
But, I love him just the same.

He never forgets my birthday.
He never forgets to call.
My Grandpa fixes everything.
My wagon and my doll.
And...
If I were a millionaire,
I'll tell you what I'd do.
I'd buy a Grandpa just like mine,
And...
Clone him
For all of you.

I love you Grandpa.

# Groovy Granny

I have a Groovy Granny.
Her name is Granny Sue.
There really isn't anything
My Granny cannot do.

She loves to ride the ferris wheel.
And shoot the water slide.
And when she bought the motor bike,
My Grandpa almost died.

She bought herself a parachute,
And jumped out of a plane.
Went crazy on a bungee cord.
Rode a river raft in Maine.

She bought herself a miniskirt.
Put six earrings in her ear.
Got herself a facelift.
Liposuction on her rear.

Bought herself a laptop.
She 'surfs' the Internet.
Went climbing on Mt. Everest,
'Bout as high as you can get.

My Granny's favourite saying is,
"Now kid, don't be a dunce.
Just live life to the fullest.
'Cause, you only go 'round once. "

# Guardian Angel

I have a Guardian Angel.
She's surrounded by a Light
That never stops protecting me,
Morning, noon and night.

She's sitting on my shoulder.
She's been there all day long.
She always watches over me.
She shows me right from wrong.

You probably can't see her,
But I will teach you how.
Just close your eyes.
Think happy thoughts.
There, do you see her now?

That's right!
She's wearing cut-off bluejeans.
There's a big 'A' on her hat.
She isn't wearing white at all.
Now, what do you think of that?

What?
You have no Guardian Angel?
I'll tell you what I'll do.
I'll say a special prayer tonight
So you can have one too.

# Hallowe'en

Hi Black Cat
Wild and hairy.
You are awesome.
You are scary.
I see you hiding in that tree.
I'm not afraid.
You can't scare me.

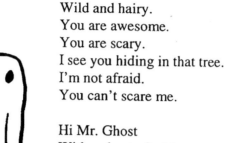

Hi Mr. Ghost
With a sheet of white.
Spooking the kids
On Hallowe'en night.
You're not real.
You're just a dream.
You can't scare me.
I won't scream.

Hi Mr. Vampire
In the mud.
Why are you always
Drinking blood?
Have you ever tried
A glass of lemonade?
Bite my neck.
I'm not afraid.

Hi Mr. Goblin
You are bad.
Behind that face
I hope it's Dad.
I hope I'm right.
I hope it's true.
I'm getting scared.
**Dad... Is that you???**

# How Long Is a Worm?

Did you ever try to measure
A slippery, wiggly worm?
Did you stick him on a ruler?
Did you hold him fast and firm?
Did you find out where his nose is?
Did you find his other end?
Did he start to wiggle faster?
Did he start to curl and bend?
Did he slide right off the ruler?
Did he cover you with 'goo'?
Well, I think I have the answer.
I'll tell you what to do.
Just 'pop' him in the freezer.
And he'll sit still for you.

# Humpty Dumpty

Humpty Dumpty was the finest of eggs.
He didn't have arms.
He didn't have legs.
He didn't play hockey.
He didn't play ball.
He just sat around
All day on a wall.

One day as he sat
And pondered his fate,
A mean little kid
Sneaked in through the gate.
He looked up and saw
Humpty sitting above.
That mean little kid
Gave poor Humpty a shove.

Humpty fell to the ground
With a terrible clatter.
He broke all apart
With a terrible splatter.

The King's horses and men
Tried to fix him with glue.
They tried string and Scotch tape
But nothing would do.

So they all sat around
And rested their legs
And enjoyed a hot breakfast
Of bacon and eggs.

# I Hate To Wear My Mittens

I hate to wear my mittens.
I hate to wear my hat.
I hate to wear my snowsuit.
It makes me look too fat.

I hate to wear my winter boots.
I hate the ice and snow.
I hate to wear long underwear.
I get itchy down below.

So please...
Someone send a warming wind.
This weather is a 'bummer'.
Turn off the deep freeze right away.
## Bring on bikini summer.

# Steven Got Even

Susie told the teacher,
"Steven's got a frog."
Steven took her lunch bag
And fed it to his dog.
**Steven Got Even!**

Tommy caught a big black bug.
Steven found it in his pants.
Tommy found his baseball cap
Filled with big red ants.
**Steven Got Even!**

Sally told the Principal,
"Steven's skipping school."
Steven got her homework
And dropped it in the pool.
**Steven Got Even!**

Mary wore a vampire mask.
She gave Steven quite a scare.
Steven told the other kids
"She's got dirty underwear."
**Steven Got Even!**

Billy got some red paint
He painted Steven's shoe.
Steven went to Billy's chair
And covered it with glue.
**Steven Got Even!**

Dana helped him with his spelling.
She shared her cookies too.
So Steven chose her first for sides,
And showed her what to do.
He helped her with her journal.
He carried Dana's books.
He told the children, "Dana's Cool,
So, no more dirty looks."
**Steven Got Even!**

# How To Catch A Dinosaur

*You Will Need:*

*1 very large cardboard box*
*1 sweet, red apple*
*1 pickup truck*
*1 bottle of lemonade*

If you want to catch a Dinosaur
You must plan ahead.
Set your clock real early
And sneak quiety out of bed.

Take your box of cardboard
Put it in the grass.
Find a spot where Dinosaurs
Are very sure to pass.

Put the apple by the box.
Make sure it's red and sweet.
'Cause Dinosaurs like apples
For an early morning treat.

Now hide behind the bushes.
Do not make a sound.
The Dinosaur will come to get
The apple on the ground.

Then sneak right up behind him
And push with all your might.
Squeeze him in the cardboard box.
Close it up real tight.

Load him in the pickup truck.
Feed him lemonade.
Then you can ride your Dinosaur
In the Santa Claus Parade.

# How To Catch A Leprechaun

*You Will Need:*

*1 giant mushroom*
*1 tube of Super Glue*
*1 pot of strawberry jam*
*1 box of sweet cookies*
*1 pot of tea*
*1 small snack table*

If you want to catch a Leprechaun
I'll tell you what to do.
Find a giant mushroom
And cover it with glue.
Then put your table right in front
With the cookies, jam and tea.
Now hide yourself.
Get out of sight,
Behind a nearby tree.
The Leprechaun will smell the jam
And come to take a bite.
When he sits down
The Super Glue
Will hold him super tight.
Then jump out fast,
And grab his nose.
Squeeze hard and really hold.
Tell him you will let him go
For his riches and his gold.
The Leprechaun will gladly trade
His treasure to be free.
Then you can buy a castle
For your Mom and Dad and Me!

# How To Catch A Polar Bear

*You Will Need:*

*1 large beach towel*
*1 long rope*
*1 bar of bubble-bath soap*
*1 polka dot bikini*

If you would catch a Polar Bear
Take away his underwear.
He'll be embarrassed,
Because his kind
Don't like to show
A bear behind.
So...
Offer him the bathing suit.
He'll slip it on, and look real cute.
Take out the towel,
Wrap him 'round,
Then sit the bear upon the ground.
Tie the bear up with the rope.
Lather him with bubble soap.
Pull him home
And wash his face.
Keep him warm
By the fireplace.
And when he dozes off to sleep,
The Polar Bear is yours to keep.

# How To Catch A Tiger Shark

*You Will Need:*

*Barbeque tongs*
*A flashlight*
*A minnow net*
*A minnow pail*
*A bowl of tender, smelly, bait fish*

If you would catch a Tiger Shark
You must go swimming after dark.
Take along your minnow net.
Swim up close as you can get.
Tempt him with his favourite dish.
A bowl of tender, smelly, fish.
When he turns 'round to take a bite,
Hold your breath with all your might.
Shine your flashlight on his nose.
Tickle his belly with your toes.
Then use your tongs to pinch his tail,
And flip him in your minnow pail.
Hide him in your swimming pool.
Next day, show all the kids at school.

# I Think I'll Eat Worms

My teacher moved my seat away
From my best friend, Sally Bass.
Now... mean old William Vanderkamp
Sits beside the prettiest girl in class.
**I Think I'll Eat Worms And Barf !**

Mr. Pointer chose Jen McGraw
To be pitcher on our team.
He says I have to play right field.
Honest... I could scream.
**I Think I'll Eat Worms And Barf !**

Ronnie Sampson got a new dirt bike.
Tommy Hodson got one too.
I'm still using training wheels.
Oh Man... That's tough to chew!
**I Think I'll Eat Worms And Barf !**

I showed my picture to Mrs. Wills.
It had a jet plane, clouds and a sun.
All she said was, "Fix it up.
And show me when you're done."
**I Think I'll Eat Worms And Barf !**

We chose up sides in Gym today.
Todd and Sarah chose.
Sarah didn't call my name.
And Todd just thumbed his nose.
**I Think I'll Eat Worms And Barf** !

Joey got a cool squirt gun
For his birthday yesterday.
I got Jockey underwear.
I'm going to run away.
**I Think I'll Eat Worms And Barf** !

Wait up!!!
Mom's making me an apple pie.
Dad says, "I'm good as gold."
I got five bucks for washing cars.

So...
**I'll Put Those Worms On Hold!**.

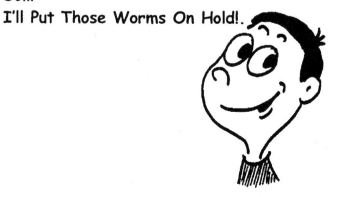

# I Wish I Had A Dinosaur

I wish I had a Dinosaur
To ride home after school.
I'd smile and wave and tip my hat,
'Oh Man', would I be cool.

I'd be the envy of the class
For every show and tell.
The kids would all 'hang out' with me,
At the recess bell.

I'd prefer a Brontosaurus
With a neck so long and tall.
But a Stegosaurus really
Wouldn't be so bad at all.

My Dinosaur will need my help
To keep him neat and tidy.
 I'd clip his nails,
And comb his tail,
And bathe him every Friday.

A Dinosaur is lots of work.
It might be 'kinda' hard
To use a 'Pooper Scooper'
To clean up our backyard.

My Mom says that a Dinosaur
Is too big for the city.

So...
I guess I'll just be satisfied
**With Maggie Sue, my Kitty.**

# If Kittycats Ruled The World

If kittycats ruled the world
What a great place this would be.
The bulldogs would have wooden legs,
And catnip would be free.

Each cat would own a little boy
To play with 'round the house.
Games like Fish, Hide and Seek,
And Pin the Tail Upon The Mouse.

Each cat would sleep in feather beds,
With downy pillows for their heads.
The birds would walk all over town
With giant boots to weigh them down.

No cat would ever have to stay,
Stuck in a cage all night and day.
Each cat would wear warm woolly socks,
And dogs would change the litter box.

Each cat would live a happy life
With his kittens and his kitty wife.
They'd cook a Sunday sparrow roast.
Each room would have a scratching post.

No kittycat would ever get
'Fixed' in the hospital by the Vet.
What a wonderful place the world would be,
In a Kittycat Democracy.

And who else would the cats elect
As President in high respect?
They'd want a leader brave and true.
Of course...
**They'd want my kitty, Maggie Sue.**

# Inventions

The scientists of the nations met
To determine, if they could,
Which invention, large or small
Gave Man the greatest good.

One thinker said, "Electricity,
It turns darkness into light."
Another said, "Eyeglasses,
They help restore our sight."

One wise man said, "The Airplane,
It takes us near and far."
Another said, "I do believe it is
the Motorcar."

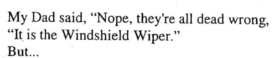

My Dad said, "Nope, they're all dead wrong,
"It is the Windshield Wiper."
But...
Mom just laughed and said,

**"No way,
It's got to be the Diaper!"**

# I'm A Desert Doggy

I'm a desert doggy
And I live in a tent.
I don't pay taxes
And I don't pay rent.

I bark at camels
And I howl at the moon.
I love to go sliding
On a sandy dune.

I'm a very happy puppy
With a very happy life.
And, someday soon
I'll have a puppydog wife.

But...
Every night I get on my knees
And pray to Heaven,
Please send me some trees.

# I'm Free

The house is quiet,
So serene.
My floors are bright,
My beds are clean.
No muddy footprints
On the floor.
No waiting
At the bathroom door.
No wet towels
On the stairs.
No stone cold dinners,
No one cares.
No underwear
Strewn 'round the hall.
No phone that rings
Right off the wall.
No blaring music
In the night.
No arguments
About who's right.
I'm an 'empty-nester'
And now,
At last I'm free!
It's party time,
Let's rumble,
'Cause...
**My daughter's off
To university!!**

# I'm So Cool

I'm so cool.
My jacket's baggy.
My hair is green.
My pants are saggy.
I've got a ring stuck in my nose.
I only wear designer clothes.
My baseball cap points to the rear.
I have six earrings in my ear.
Every Friday I skip school.
In class, I always act the fool.
I give my word, but never call.
I 'hang out' weekends at the mall.
Some people say that I am spoiled.
Some say my brain is fried or boiled.
But that's not true,
It's just a phase.
It's just a fashion.
Just a craze.
Just have patience.
Have sympathy.
'Cause...

**My Dad was once
      a kid like me.**

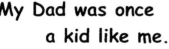

# It's Tough To Be A Hockey Dad

It's tough to be a Hockey Dad,
I never get to sleep.
I'm always on the road by four,
With eight kids in my Jeep.

It's tough to be a Hockey Dad.
The arena's always freezing.
I spend all winter with the flu.
Coughing, choking, sneezing.

It's tough to be a Hockey Dad.
Running bingos, breathing smoke.
My Christmas dinner every year,
Is a hot dog and a Coke.

It's tough to be a Hockey Dad,
With chocolate bars to sell.
Praying that someday my kid,
Will make the N. H. L.
But...
I guess it's really not so tough.
There's one job just as bad.
That's...
To be a caring Hockey Mom,
Who loves a Hockey Dad.

# John, John The Leprechaun

I'm John, John the Leprechaun.
I'm from the Emerald Isle.
I'm John, John the Leprechaun,
I have a Shamrock smile.

I'm John, John the Leprechaun.
I never will grow old.
Just grab my toe,
And... don't let go,
You'll find my pot of gold.

I'm John, John the Leprechaun.
It's "Erin Go Bragh", I say.
May the Saints protect you.
May the devil neglect you.
I love Saint Patrick's Day.

# Just Treat Me Nice

Please don't turn your back on me.
Please don't call me names.
Please don't choose me last of all
For sides, in schoolyard games.

Please don't snicker at my clothes.
Please don't pull my hair.
Please don't ignore me all the time.
Please always treat me fair.

Please don't let schoolmates laugh at me.
Please tell them we are friends.
Then we can meet in Heaven
Where friendship never ends.

# Mommy Do You Love Me?

Mommy, do you love me?
Why, of course I do dear!
Let's snuggle a minute,
Come, sit down over here.

I prayed every bedtime,
For a little girl like you,
And when I saw your funny face,
No one else would do!

Your face was all wrinkled,
Your skin was all red.
You were bald as a beach ball,
Not a hair on your head.

You cried and you yelled.
You burped and you spit.
You threw the odd tantrum.
You took the odd fit.

But you're growing up quickly,
And soon you'll take flight.
And I'll be alone
With my memories each night.

So, you ask, "DO I LOVE YOU?"
My answer is simple.
I love every freckle.
I love every dimple.
I love every giggle.
I love every smile.
You're my reason for living.

You make life worthwhile.
Together we'll travel life's road to the end.

**Sweetheart, You're my Daughter!**

# Mrs. Claus

I get up bright and early
Christmas Eve is here once more.
Santa Claus is snoring
Behind the bedroom door.

I wash and iron his new red suit.
I lay out his underwear.
I pack his lunch with sandwiches,
An apple and a pear.

I check the light on Rudolph's nose.
I make sure each reindeer's fed.
I help load all the presents
On Santa's magic sled.

And when, at last he's ready
To take off on his leave,
A kiss goodbye, and then I sit
Alone on Christmas Eve.

He gets all the glory.
I get no applause.
Because his name is Santa,
And I'm just Mrs. Claus.

But, from now on each Christmas Eve,
I won't miss him, not at all.
'Cause, as soon as Santa leaves the Pole
**I'm going shopping at the mall.**

# Mrs. Drew

Mrs. Drew, I'm begging you,
To help me right away.
Robert Green just spit on me.
He does it everyday.

He also took my pencil case.
He threw it in the dirt.
He called me names, like Little Wimp,
Momma's Boy, and Squirt.

He took my ball at recess.
He tossed it on the roof.
He pushed my face down in the mud.
He broke my wisdom tooth.

Mrs. Drew, I'm begging you.
Robert Green's a goon.
Send Robert Green, 'THE BULLY MACHINE',
On a rocket to the moon!

# My Dad Will Be Mad

I thought I saw
My Mommy
With Santa Claus
Last night.

She was standing
Close beside him.
He hugged her,
Really tight.

Mom tickled
Santa's belly.
She kissed
His snow-white head.
I'm going to tell
My Father.
As soon as Dad
Gets out of bed.

# My Favourite Dog

I love all the dogs
That are furry.
I love all the dogs
That are fun.
But...
The dog
I love best
Above all the rest
Is...
A juicy Hot Dog
In a bun.

# Tantrums

I threw a tantrum yesterday.
It always helps me get my way.
I pick my spot, I pick my time,
To start my ugly pantomime!

Last week they ordered me to bed,
But I preferred T.V. instead.
So I broke stuff around the house,
Until they turned on Mickey Mouse.

I hold my breath 'til I am blue.
My folks don't know just what to do.
And when I yell and start to shake,
They rush to get me chocolate cake.

My Mom gives in and takes me shopping.
I know just how to keep her hopping.
I scream and shout and bang the wall,
Until I get a Barbie doll.

Mondays I won't go to school.
I act as stubborn as a mule.
I kick and punch and pout and blow,
Until it is too late to go.

My Dad says I am such a brat.
I really can't agree with that.
My mental health is really fine,
**Gee whiz, I'm only 29!**

# My Four Leaf Clover

I found a four leaf clover
Covered with morning dew.
My Dad said, "Don't lose it son,
It will bring good luck to you."

My good luck started yesterday.
I scored the winning goal.
I got an 'A' in history.
I made the Honour Roll.

I got a raise in my allowance.
I won the 'track meet mile'.
The kids say, "I'm class president."
And... Becky loves my smile.

My Dad said, "Son, that clover leaf
Will only go so far.
Then... It's just hard work
That will bring you luck,
And...
**The kinda guy you are."**

# My Grandma

My Grandma is a super friend.
They say I have her eyes.
Whenever Grandma visits us
She brings me a surprise.

They say that Gram is spoiling me
Well, maybe that is true.
But that's what Grandmas everywhere
Are really s'posed to do.

One day she brought a Barbie doll.
One day she brought a kitty.
One day she picked me up at school,
And took me to the city.

We window shopped.
We laughed a lot.
We 'hung out' at the mall.
My Grandma is the 'coolest' Gram,
Of any Gram at all.

My Grandma says
I'm much more fun,
Than my Mom or Uncle Jack.
'Cause...
When my Gram is all worn out,

**She can give me back.**

# My Kitty

My kitty gives me love licks
To let me know she cares.
But...
When she snuggles close to me
I'm chewing kitty hairs.

My kitty sleeps in bed with me
Right on my pillow case.
She always flops down happily
With her butt stuck in my face.

My kitty likes to eat with me
She sits up on my chair.
Sometimes she shows me dirty paws
But really, I don't care.

My kitty begs for table scraps.
Mom says, "Please don't give her more."
'Cause every time I sneak her some
She throws up on the floor.

My kitty is my special friend.
She never lets me down.
She's always waiting at the door
When I come home from town.

I really love my kitty.
She's an angel brave and true.
Why don't you ask your Mommy
To get a kittycat for you?

# My Tree House

I'm going to build a tree house.
I'll build it way up high.
At night I'll watch
A million stars
Decorate the sky.

I'll sleep snug in a sleeping bag.
I'll wear my warm nightgown.
I'll have one ladder going up
And... a ladder going down.

Only girls will be allowed.
The sign says, "Boys Keep Out".
I'll have the coolest 'pad' in town.
I haven't any doubt.

But...
If it gets too spooky
Or I see a furry mouse
I'll crawl into my Mother's bed
Safe inside our house.

# New Baby

My Dad said, "It's a big surprise,
We're getting something new.
When your Mom gets home from the hospital
She'll bring a pal for you."

Mom came home with a baby boy.
I wasn't that impressed.
I didn't like the way he smelled
Or the funny way he dressed.

His face was red and wrinkled.
Not a hair upon his head.
He couldn't play Nintendo.
He kicked and squirmed in bed.

He wasn't fun at dinner time.
He couldn't sing or dance.
And when he started screaming,
I knew he 'peed' his pants.

I'm going to grab that baby,
And stuff him in a sack.
I'll load him in a pick-up truck.
**That baby's going back!!!**

# Ologies

An entomologist likes bugs.
A carpetologist likes rugs.
An anthropologist likes apes.
A jellyologist likes grapes.
A biologist likes germs.
A wigglyologist likes worms.
A geologist likes rocks.
A toe-toeologist likes socks.
A seismologist likes 'quakes'.
But,
I'm a tummyologist...
**I like cakes!**

59

# Red Beard The Pirate

They call me old Red Beard the Pirate.
I'm the captain of my pirate ship.
From Jamaica to Dover,
I roam the world over
With a sword and a gun and a whip.

It's not easy being a pirate.
I don't get to cuddle my Mom.
There's no birthday cake,
No chocolate milkshake,
I never get asked to the prom.

My white shirts are all 'sorta' dingy.
They never get washed in the bleach.
I don't get to 'rassle'
Or build a sand castle,
Or look for neat shells on the beach.

Yes, they call me old Red Beard the Pirate.
But I'm growing much older each day,
Now my beard is not red,
There's no hair on my head,
And my big belly gets in the way.

So... it's goodbye to Red Beard the Pirate.
My time to retire is due.
I'll be happy, content,
Just paying the rent,
And...
**Changing a diaper or two.**

# Rocks

Big rocks, hard rocks
Rolling 'round the yard rocks.
Cold rocks, old rocks
Rocks are lots of fun.

Hot rocks, pet rocks.
Slimy, slippery wet rocks.
June rocks, dune rocks.
Basking in the sun.

Lava rocks, space rocks.
Lumpy lunar base rocks.
Asteroids, meteors
Flashing 'cross the sky.

Candy rocks, dandy rocks
Covered up with sandy rocks.
Skip 'em 'cross the wave rocks.
Watch 'em as they fly.

Fake rocks, lake rocks.
Groovy shake and bake rocks.
Bedrocks, red rocks.
All across the land.

You can keep your cool rocks.
Lock 'em in the school rocks.
Give me good old diamond rocks.
Sparkling on my hand.

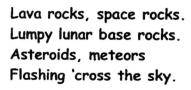

# Supermarket Mom

I went to the Mom Supermarket
To pick out the best Mom of all.
She should know how to 'rassle'
And build a sand castle,
And dribble a 'cool' basketball.

I saw Moms of all shapes and sizes.
Some short, some tall and some wide.
Some dressed in bluejeans.
Some pretty as Queens.
They lined up and stood side by side.

My new Mom would have to be beautiful,
And cook all the pies that I like.
Everyday she would bake,
Some cookies and cake,
And buy me that new mountain bike.

She'd have to know lots about hockey,
And not scold me when I am late.
She must know what to do
When I've got the flu,
And keep broccoli off of my plate.

I saw many Moms at the market.
And all of those Mothers looked fine.
But my shopping is done
'Cause... My Mom's number one
**The Best Mom is already mine**.

## I love you Mom!

# Watch Cat

My Maggie Sue's a Watch Cat.
She guards my house at night.
She frightens all the bad guys,
With a scratch,
A kick,
A bite.

She's a Black Belt Star at Judo.
She's good at Kung Fu too,
But she's wonderful with children.
My super Maggie Sue.

I'd never trade my kitty,
For a silent house alarm.
With Maggie Sue on duty
I sleep just like a charm.

Woe betide the 'critter',
That sneaks into my house.
She stalks the 'varmint' quietly.
Oops... there goes another mouse.

I really love my Maggie Sue,
But... she won't come when I call.
And, just one time it would be nice,
**If she would fetch the ball.**

# Prudence Prim

Prudence Prim marched down the street.
Her shoes were clean.
Her dress was neat.
Her hair was combed.
Her nails were done.
Her white teeth sparkled
In the sun.

She happened on Bad Billy Budd,
Who pushed poor Prudence in the mud.
Prudence didn't whine or cry,
She looked Bad Billy in the eye.
She promptly grabbed him by the shirt,
And rubbed his face down in the dirt.

"Take that, Bad Billy Budd," she said.
"Don't try to bully me.
You'd better learn your lesson fast
Or you'll be history."

Prudence turned, and walked away.
She gave a knowing wink.
Billly learned the hard way,
Girls are stronger than you think.

# Love My Braces, "Not"

Those T.V. ads with smiling faces
Of smiling kids,
With big steel braces,
Would have us think
Kids really care,
'Bout squirming in the dentist's chair.
BUT...
I have news that you should know.
Contrary to that T.V. show,
Kids hate those picks and probes and pokes.
Kids hate their mouths filled up with spokes.
Kids hate the look of steel-mesh braces,
Designed to fill up empty spaces.
Kids don't enjoy a drill that whines,
Or a mouth that looks like Frankenstein's.
Kids really do endure those braces,
To change their look.
To change their faces.
For years from now,
When the 'kissin's' great,
They won't be embarassed by,
A denture plate.

# Goldilocks

A cool looking blond
With curly gold hair,
Went into the forest
Searching for bear.

She walked a long way,
'Til her 'toe-toes' were sore.
When she saw a small house,
So... she opened the door.

Nobody answered.
No one was there.
She sat down to rest,
And broke a small chair.

She ran into the kitchen
And found porridge hot,
She got out a spoon,
And ate the whole pot.

She went to the bedroom,
And found a small bed,
She snuggled down 'comfy',
And lay down her head.

She dreamed something furry
Stood over her there.
She opened her eyes.
'Holy Mackerel'... a Bear!

She jumped to her feet,
And gave a loud shout.
She ran to the doorway
And hurried on out.

The Three Bears sat down
On the front porch and talked.
"From now on," said the Papa,
**"We will keep
   our door locked."**

# Where Does Gorilla Go When It Rains?

Where does Gorilla go when it rains?
Does he hide in the jungle?
Does he run on the plains?
Does he put on a raincoat
And splash down the street?
Does he have rubber boots
To cover his feet?
Does he sleep in the valley?
Does he play in the zoo?
Well...
Here's a big secret.
I'll share it with you.
**Gorilla goes wherever
Gorilla wants to!**

# Index